HALF A SIXPENCE

A MUSICAL PLAY

Based on the Novel "Kipps" by H. G. WELLS

MUSIC AND LYRICS BY

DAVID HENEKER

BOOK BY

BEVERLEY CROSS

All applications for performance by Amateur Societies must be made in advance to:

The Really Useful Group Ltd.
22 Tower Street, London WC2H 9NS
Tel: 071-240-0880

© 1963 & 1967 Britannia Music Co. Ltd.
International Music Publications Limited
Griffin House 161 Hammersmith Road
London W6 8BS England.

HALF A SIXPENCE

CHARACTERS

ARTHUR KIPPS	An apprentice shopman. An orphan
SID PORNICK	Also an apprentice. A Socialist
BUGGINS	Another apprentice. A pessimist
PEARCE	The fourth apprentice. A dandy
FLO BATES	A shopgirl
VICTORIA	
KATE	Three shopgirls
EMMA	
MR. SHALFORD	The owner of the Emporium
MR. CARSHOT	Head floor walker
MRS. WALSINGHAM	A customer
MRS. BOTTING	Mother of Helen
ANN	Sid's sister
CHESTER COOTE	
HARRY CHITTERLOW	An Actor playwright
LAURA	A barmaid
HELEN WALSINGHAM	
EDITH	A lady student
A BEARDED STUDENT	
YOUNG WALSINGHAM	Helen's spoiled brother. A lawyer
PHOTOGRAPHER	
REPORTER	
GWENDOLIN	A cheeky parlourmaid
MR. WILKINS	

SHOPGIRLS, CUSTOMERS, STUDENTS

First performance, presented by Harold Fielding, at the Cambridge Theatre, London, on 21st March, 1963 with TOMMY STEELE as "Kipps"

———————

SYNOPSIS

The action takes place in Folkestone in the year 1900

Overture

ACT I

ACT II

MUSICAL PROGRAMME

HALF A SIXPENCE

No 1

OVERTURE

Music and Lyrics by
DAVID HENEKER

MADE IN ENGLAND
12131

Britannia

Britannia

4

Act I

MORNING MUSIC (Opening Sequence)

8

Britannia

SHOP BALLET

11

Britannia

Dialogue

Britannia

"ECONOMY"

Cue: KIPPS: "One day we'll show 'im ....."

16

Britannia

18

12131   Britannia

Britannia

Nº 4

DUET – (Kipps and Ann)
"HALF A SIXPENCE"

Cue: ANN: "Don't be silly, kissing's soft . . . ."

Britannia

22

12131   Britannia

No. 4ᴬ   SCENE CHANGE (2–3)

Britannia

№ 5

SCENE CHANGE (3–3ᴬ)

Cue: CHITTERLOW: "He'll see you right" (*Exit*)

№ 6

SONG— (Kipps and Mens' Chorus)
"MONEY TO BURN"

Cue: KIPPS: "I'd buy a banjo"

Britannia

30

12131   Britannia

Britannia

32

Britannia

36

Britannia

38

Britannia

MEN

Down to the Town, to buy a ban-jo, Bring on the girls, and a-way we go!

Britannia

42

12131

Britannia

46

SCENE CHANGE (4-5)

SCENE CHANGE (5-6)

Cue: CHITTERLOW: "You look perfectly respectable to me" *(Blackout)*

Andante moderato

SCENE CHANGE (6-7)

Nᴼ 9

Cue: SHALFORD: "Hot water bottle, roast chicken, a day off. Nothing...." *(Lights fade)*

Valse moderato

SONG—(Ann and Shopgirls)
"I DON'T BELIEVE A WORD OF IT"

Cue: KATE: Not nice— not nice at all! Philandering

54

Dialogue
Britannia

Nº 10

SCENE CHANGE (7-8)

Cue: KIPPS: " and that to your blessed economy !" (*Black out*)

SONG- (Kipps and Chorus)
"A PROPER GENTLEMAN"

Cue: SID: "Twelve hundred a year"

Bright tempo

Britannia

SONG-(Kipps)

"SHE'S TOO FAR ABOVE ME"

Slow Waltz

Cue: HELEN: Au revoir *(She exits)* · Kipps examines card · *(Reads)* "Miss Helen Walsingham Bachelor of Arts" *(Sighs) Sings*

She's too far a-bove me by half___ she is,___ She'd laugh,___ she would,___ Not half___ she would, If I were to say I loved her so,___ 'Cause I

Britannia

63

12131

Segue
Britannia

Nº 12ᴬ

SCENE CHANGE (8—9)

L'istesso tempo   *(Fade when scene opens)*

Dialogue

No. 13   SONG – (Kipps and Chorus)
"IF THE RAIN'S GOT TO FALL"

Cue: HELEN: "And Arthur, don't worry, it won't rain" (*she kisses Kipps and exits*)

66

12131

Britannia

68

Segue as one

Britannia

№ 13A

DANCE
"IF THE RAIN'S GOT TO FALL"

Britannia

74

12131   Britannia

Segue

No 14   SONG—(Chorus)
"THE OLD MILITARY CANAL"

12131   Britannia

78

12131   Britannia

80

12131   Britannia

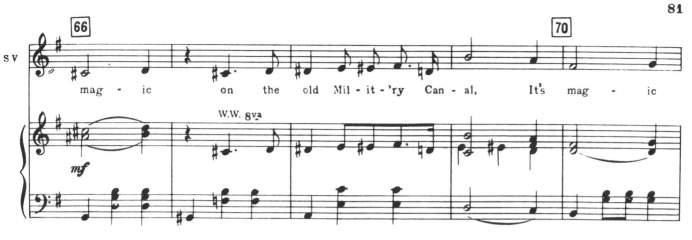

magic on the old Mil-it-'ry Can-al, It's mag - ic

that the old Mil-it-r'y Can-al, Though scen - ic, Is just slight - ly

un - hy-gen - ic, You'll a - gree?

Chorus
(Toughs)

S

A

T

B

It's

Brass

82

84

№ 14 A.

MILITARY CANAL UNDERSCORE

Cue: KIPPS: 'Appey, 'Elen?
HELEN: "Wonderfully!"

Valse Moderato

Dialogue continues
Britannia

No 15   FINALE–ACT 1

Cue: HELEN:"Arthur, please!" *(as they touch hands the rain starts)*
HELEN: *(speaks)* "Will you take me in? I think it is beginning to rain"

End of Act 1
Britannia

N⁰ 16   ENTR'ACTE

Britannia

90

Dialogue
Britannia

Act II

DUET – (Kipps and Chitterlow)
"THE ONE WHO'S RUN AWAY"

Cue: CHITTERLOW: "There's plenty of fish in the sea."

Britannia

Britannia

Nº 17

SOLARIUM DANCE

Britannia

98

100

Cut when Kipps crashes into Guests

Short Dialogue

№ 18   SCENE CHANGE (2–3)

Cue: HELEN: "And I loved him just the way he was." (*Exits*)

Britannia

Nº 18ᴬ

DUET (Ann and Kipps)
"LONG AGO"

Cue: KIPPS "Oh…. I do love you, Ann."

Slowly, with feeling

ANN *(speaks)* "I love you too, Artie. I s'pose I always have."

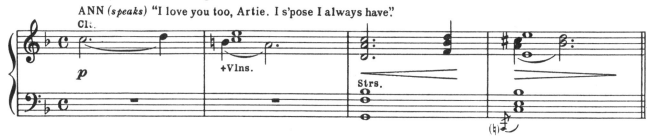

Ann *(Sings)*
I was long-ing to tell you long a-go, _____ So

ANN
long a-go, _____ But how could I tell you? I was

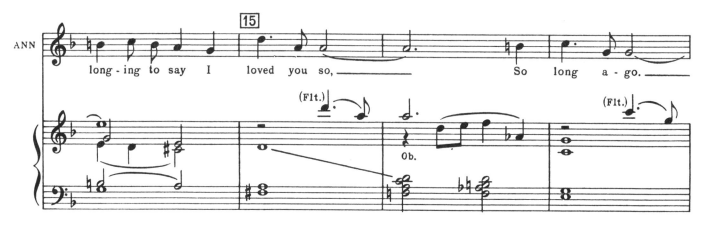

ANN
long-ing to say I loved you so, _____ So long a-go. _____

SCENE CHANGE (3–4)

№ 19

Espressivo

Segue

Dialogue

Britannia

108

Britannia

112

113

12131   Britannia

114

12131

Britannia

№ 20A

FLASH, BANG, WALLOP! – EXIT

Dialogue

№ 21

SCENE CHANGE (4–5)

Cue: SID: "Ha! Fat lot of good it'll do *him!*" (*Exits*)
FLO: "Sidney, wait for me!"

Dialogue

No 22

SONG— (Ann)
"I KNOW WHAT I AM"

Cue: KIPPS:"Your going to 'ave eleven bedrooms, and like 'em!" (*Exits*)

118

№ 23   SCENE CHANGE (5-6)

№ 23A   SCENE CHANGE (6-7)

Cue: KIPPS: "You wait till you see it"

Britannia

Nº 24   SONG — (Kipps and Ensemble)
"THE PARTY'S ON THE HOUSE"

Cue: KIPPS: "I was counting on you to cheer me up" — "Come on, en-

122

Britannia

126

128

scene; _____ You're gon-na wake to find there's no-thing to clean! _____

Come on, en-joy your-selves, ___ the par - ty's on the house, the

130

The par-ty's on the house, tho' there ain't no house!
We're

gon-na raise the roof, tho' there ain't no roof!
There's

High-hat cymbal

All (Spoken)

Vlas. Trom. Cello   Tpts. Cl.

Tpts. Cls.

+ Tpt. W.W.

Trom. Cello

12131   Britannia

132

12131   Britannia

134

Britannia

PARTY EXIT – (Ensemble)

REPRISE — (Kipps and Ann) and CAROL SEQUENCE (Chorus)
"HALF A SIXPENCE"

Cue: ANN "But at least we both got our tokens"

Britannia

144

No 28

FINALE— (Ensemble)

12131

Britannia

146

51 Broadly

ALL
-brel-la.

55 Bright 2

ALL
All lined up in a wed-ding group, Here we are for a pho-to-graph.

W.W.
mf Cello

60

ALL
All dressed up in a morn-ing suit, And we're try-ing not to laugh. Since the

65

ALL
ear-ly cave-man, in his fun, took a trip to Gret-na Green, There's

W.W.

148

12131   Britannia

Segue after applause
Britannia

FINALE ULTIMO— (Ensemble)

152

Britannia

End of Opera

Britannia

№ 30

PLAY-OUT

Britannia